Up to You, Sam

Chris Powling

Illustrated by
Jane Bottomley

OXFORD
UNIVERSITY PRESS

"You can have a cat," said Mum.

"Or a dog," said Dad.

"It's up to you, Sam," they said.

"It's up to me?" I said. "OK, I'd like a gorilla."

"A gorilla?" said Mum and Dad.
"A big gorilla," I said.

"Are you mad?" said Mum.
"No gorilla, OK?" said Dad.

"But it's up to me," I said. "You said so."

Mum looked at Dad. Dad looked at Mum.
"OK," they said. "You can have a gorilla."

"I can?" I said.

"It's up to you, Sam," they said.

"Come on, then!" I said. "Let's go!"

So we went to get a gorilla.

9

We went in this shop. We went in that shop.

We went in shop after shop after shop.

We looked for a gorilla all day.
"See?" said Mum. "No gorilla."

"Sorry, Sam," Dad said.

a dog is

a friend
for life!

I was so fed up. "OK," I said at
last. "I'll have a cat or a dog."

"It's up to you, Sam," said Mum
and Dad.

"A dog," I said. "I'd like a dog."

"Let's go to one more shop then," they said.

Pups

So we did...